Y0-BYZ-951

Language Arts
Mix & Match GAMES
grade 1

100 ways to practice key language arts skills!

- ◎ Rhyming
- ◎ Initial Consonants
- ◎ Initial Consonant Blends
- ◎ Long *a*
- ◎ Initial Consonant Digraphs

- ◎ Word Families
- ◎ Word Order
- ◎ Vocabulary
- ◎ Plural Nouns
- ◎ Antonyms

Ready to play in minutes!

Managing Editor: Lynn Drolet

Editorial Team: Becky S. Andrews, Diane Badden, Kimberley Bruck, Karen A. Brudnak, Kathy Coop, Pam Crane, Lynette Dickerson, Sarah Foreman, Theresa Lewis Goode, Tazmen Hansen, Marsha Heim, Lori Z. Henry, Debra Liverman, Dorothy C. McKinney, Thad H. McLaurin, Sharon Murphy, Jennifer Nunn, Gerri Primak, Mark Rainey, Greg D. Rieves, Hope Rodgers, Rebecca Saunders, Donna K. Teal, Zane Williard

www.themailbox.com

©2008 The Mailbox®
All rights reserved.
ISBN10 #1-56234-804-3 • ISBN13 #978-156234-804-5

Printed in China
10 9 8 7 6 5 4 3 2 1

Table of Contents

☆ Relaxing Ride

☆ Party Time!

☆ Loop-the-Loop

☆ Book Buddies

☆ Happy Hopper

☆ Super Sleuth

☆ Leaping on Lily Pads

☆ To the Moon!

☆ Going for a Swim

☆ Play Ball!

What's Inside

Relaxing Ride

Put task card here.

Directions for two players:
1. Put the task card on the gameboard.
2. Stack the game cards facedown.
3. Put your markers on START.
4. In turn, draw a game card and give your answer.
5. If your answer is correct, roll the die and move.
6. The first player to reach FINISH wins.

START

Your raft wobbles. Move back one space.

Paddle with your feet. Move ahead one space.

FINISH

Hope you had a nice ride!

Ten full-color gameboards!

Ten sets of game cards that can be used with every gameboard!

Rhyming

Initial consonants

Initial consonant blends

Long *a*

Initial consonant digraphs

Word families

Word order

Vocabulary

Plural nouns

Antonyms

Plus skill assessments, game markers, and more

Name _____   Date _____

Score
10

Circle the rhymes.

Language Arts Mix & Match Games • ©The Mailbox® Books • TEC61127 • Key p. 14

Assessment 1   **Rhyming**

- -

Name _____   Date _____

Rhyming

Score
10

Circle the rhymes.

Language Arts Mix & Match Games • ©The Mailbox® Books • TEC61127 • Key p. 14

4   **Assessment 2**   **Rhyming**

Name _____   Date _____

Initial Consonants

Score 10

Circle the beginning letter.

s f v	h l d	h w n	l r w	f v s
b v p	l g d	w f v	m n w	p b z

Language Arts Mix & Match Games • ©The Mailbox® Books • TEC61127 • Key p. 14

Assessment 1   **Initial consonants**

- -

Name _____   Date _____

Initial Consonants

Score 10

Circle the beginning letter.

h b w	m d n	g h c	y r t	v f z
d n g	y h w	d p b	l h d	v z s

Language Arts Mix & Match Games • ©The Mailbox® Books • TEC61127 • Key p. 14

Assessment 2   **Initial consonants**   5

Name _____   Date _____

Score
10

Circle the beginning blend.

gl gr cl	st sw sp	pr bl br	fl fr bl	cr tr dr
sp sn sm	bl pl gl	sk sn sm	cl gr cr	st sl sp

Language Arts Mix & Match Games • ©The Mailbox® Books • TEC61127 • Key p. 14

Assessment 1   **Initial consonant blends**

Name _____   Date _____

Initial Consonant Blends

Score
10

Circle the beginning blend.

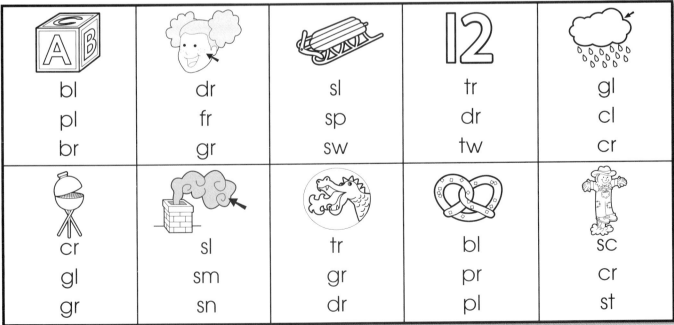

bl pl br	dr fr gr	sl sp sw	tr dr tw	gl cl cr
cr gl gr	sl sm sn	tr gr dr	bl pr pl	sc cr st

Language Arts Mix & Match Games • ©The Mailbox® Books • TEC61127 • Key p. 14

Initial consonant blends

Name _____   Date _____

Long a

Circle the word that has the long **a** sound as in .

had	hay	made	gas	pain
rake	that	mad	gate	pack
ate	cap	stay	wax	tap
glad	waist	pad	wave	claim

Language Arts Mix & Match Games • ©The Mailbox® Books • TEC61127 • Key p. 14

Assessment 1   **Long *a***

- -

Name _____   Date _____

Long a

Score 10

Circle the word that has the long **a** sound as in .

make	cast	skate	tray	back
back	wait	rash	rat	brain
pad	lake	map	cap	day
date	grab	paint	cape	past

Language Arts Mix & Match Games • ©The Mailbox® Books • TEC61127 • Key p. 14

Assessment 2   **Long *a*** 7

Name _____ Date _____

Initial Consonant Digraphs

Circle the letters that make the beginning sound.

ch th sh wh	ch th sh wh	ch th sh wh	ch th sh wh	ch th sh wh
ch th sh wh	ch th sh wh	ch th sh wh	ch th sh wh	ch th sh wh

Language Arts Mix & Match Games • ©The Mailbox® Books • TEC61127 • Key p. 14

Assessment 1   **Initial consonant digraphs**

- -

Name _____ Date _____

Initial Consonant Digraphs

Circle the letters that make the beginning sound.

ch th sh wh	ch th sh wh	ch th sh wh	ch th sh wh	ch th sh wh
ch th sh wh	ch th sh wh	ch th sh wh	ch th sh wh	ch th sh wh

Language Arts Mix & Match Games • ©The Mailbox® Books • TEC61127 • Key p. 14

8 **Assessment 2**   **Initial consonant digraphs**

Name _____   Date _____

Word Families

Score
10

Circle the letter or letters that make a word.

__ag	__an	__ay	__eed	__at
b k	y v	sk cl	w z	fl sn
__um	__ink	__uck	__ell	__op
p h	bl gr	d n	br sh	n m

Language Arts Mix & Match Games • ©The Mailbox® Books • TEC61127 • Key p. 14

Assessment 1   **Word families**

- -

Name _____   Date _____

Word Families

Score
10

Circle the letter or letters that make a word.

__est	__ick	__ip	__an	__ill
s b	bl st	fr gr	f y	v h
__ot	__at	__in	__ine	__ap
g z	cl th	sm sk	l r	tr dr

Language Arts Mix & Match Games • ©The Mailbox® Books • TEC61127 • Key p. 14

Assessment 2   **Word families**   9

Name _____ Date _____

Word Order

Write numbers to show the word order for each sentence.

__ I __ run. __ to __ like	__ dog __ The __ black. __ is	__ has __ kite. __ He __ a	__ fox __ can __ The __ hide.	__ sand. __ in the __ I __ shells __ see
__ There __ cups __ are __ table. __ on the	__ sleeps __ The __ mat. __ on the __ cat	__ Let's __ in __ run __ the __ sun.	__ rat __ fat __ The __ cheese. __ ate	__ a __ song. __ can __ sing __ I

Language Arts Mix & Match Games • ©The Mailbox® Books • TEC61127 • Key p. 14

Assessment 1   **Word order**

- -

Name _____ Date _____

Word Order

Write numbers to show the word order for each sentence.

__ fish __ can __ The __ swim.	__ like __ I __ jump. __ to	__ bike. __ has __ a __ She	__ The __ green. __ is __ frog	__ in the __ have __ I __ bag. __ hats
__ pigs __ in the __ The __ mud. __ are	__ see __ grass. __ bugs __ in the __ I	__ had __ We __ lunch. __ for __ fries	__ deck. __ play __ the __ Let's __ on	__ read __ I __ at __ books __ home.

Language Arts Mix & Match Games • ©The Mailbox® Books • TEC61127 • Key p. 14

Word order

Name _____ Date _____

Vocabulary

Draw an **X** on the word that does not belong.

bird mug cat dog	ship bus plane hut	bike mat yo-yo ball	sun star van moon	jeep mad happy sad
corn moo quack bark	ham bell pizza chicken	tree wish weed grass	sled finger toe nose	hen duck doll horse

Language Arts Mix & Match Games • ©The Mailbox® Books • TEC61127 • Key p. 14

Assessment 1   **Vocabulary**

- -

Name _____ Date _____

Vocabulary

Draw an **X** on the word that does not belong.

red bag yellow green	apple lemon grape mitten	horse pig cup duck	vest crab sand shell	shirt pants coat frog
pan pot nut dish	cry rope smile frown	cup fork plate jump	pen crayon marker egg	dog hand foot elbow

Language Arts Mix & Match Games • ©The Mailbox® Books • TEC61127 • Key p. 14

Assessment 2   **Vocabulary** 11

Name _____   Date _____

Plural Nouns

Score 10

Circle the word if it means more than one.

bus	trees	mice	vine	feet
boxes	grapes	log	maps	house

Language Arts Mix & Match Games • ©The Mailbox® Books • TEC61127 • Key p. 14

Assessment 1   **Plural nouns**

- -

Name _____   Date _____

Plural Nouns

Score 10

Circle the word if it means more than one.

pig	teeth	skates	dress	bags
roses	bugs	grill	ducks	fox

Language Arts Mix & Match Games • ©The Mailbox® Books • TEC61127 • Key p. 14

Assessment 2   **Plural nouns**

Name _____   Date _____

Antonyms

Circle the words if they are opposites.

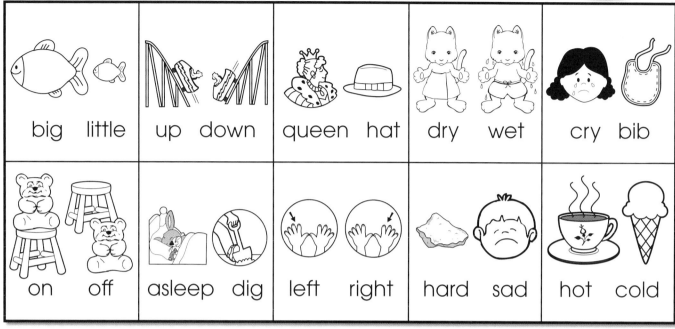

big little	up down	queen hat	dry wet	cry bib
on off	asleep dig	left right	hard sad	hot cold

Language Arts Mix & Match Games • ©The Mailbox® Books • TEC61127 • Key p. 14

Assessment 1   **Antonyms**

- -

Name _____   Date _____

Antonyms

Circle the words if they are opposites.

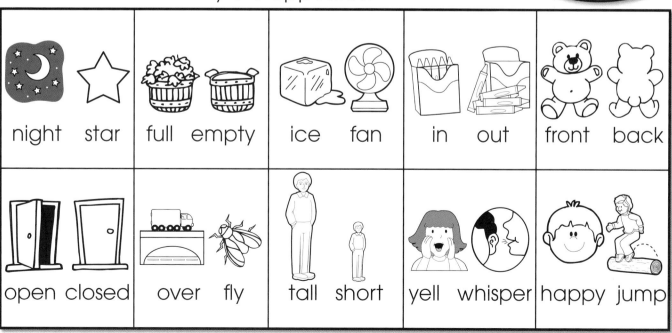

night star	full empty	ice fan	in out	front back
open closed	over fly	tall short	yell whisper	happy jump

Language Arts Mix & Match Games • ©The Mailbox® Books • TEC61127 • Key p. 14

Assessment 2   **Antonyms** 13

Assessment Answer Keys

Page 4

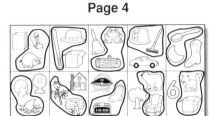

Page 5

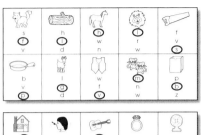

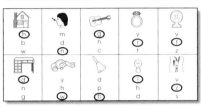

Page 6

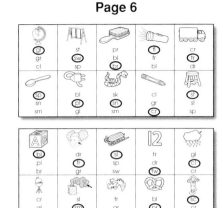

Page 7

had	hay	made	gas	pain
rake	that	mad	gate	pack
ate	cap	stay	wax	tap
glad	waist	pad	wave	claim

cake	cast	skate	tray	back
back	wait	rash	rat	brain
pad	lake	map	cap	day
date	grab	paint	cape	past

Page 8

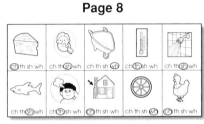

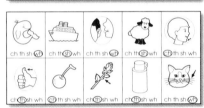

Page 9

__ag	__an	__ay	__eed	__at
b k	y v	sk cl	w z	fl sn
__um	__ink	__uck	__ell	__op
p h	bl gr	d n	br sh	n m

__est	__ick	__ip	__an	__ill
s b	bl st	fr gr	f y	v h
__ot	__at	__in	__ine	__ap
g z	cl th	sm sk	l r	fr dr

Page 10

1 I	2 dog	2 has	2 fox	5 sand.
4 run	1 The	4 kite	3 can	4 in the
3 to	4 black	1 He	1 the	1 I
2 like	3 is	3 a	4 hide.	3 shells
				2 see

1 There	3 sleeps	1 Let's	3 rat	4 a
3 cups	1 The	3 in	2 fat	5 song
2 are	5 mat	2 run	1 The	2 can
5 table.	4 on the	4 the	5 cheese.	3 sing
4 on the	2 cat		5 sun.	1 I

2 fish	2 like	4 bike	1 The	4 in the
3 can	1 I	2 has	4 green.	2 have
1 The	4 jump	3 a	3 is	1 I
4 swim	3 to	1 She	2 frog	5 bag.
				3 hats

2 pigs	2 see	2 had	5 deck	2 read
4 in the	5 grass	1 We	2 play	1 I
1 The	3 bugs	5 lunch.	4 the	4 at
5 mud	4 in the	4 for	1 Let's	3 books
3 are	1 I	3 fries	3 on	5 home.

Page 11

Page 12

bus	trees	mice	vine	feet
boxes	grapes	log	maps	house

pig	teeth	skates	dress	bags
roses	bugs	grill	ducks	fox

Page 13

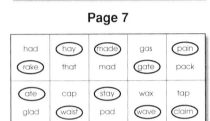

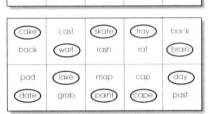

Skills Tracker
Language Arts Mix & Match Games

Name _____

Skills	Assessment Checkup 1		Assessment Checkup 2		Notes
	Score	Date	Score	Date	
Rhyming					
Initial Consonants					
Initial Consonant Blends					
Long *a*					
Initial Consonant Digraphs					
Word Families					
Word Order					
Vocabulary					
Plural Nouns					
Antonyms					

Language Arts Mix & Match Games • ©The Mailbox® Books • TEC61127

Note to the teacher: Personalize a copy of this page for every student and organize the copies in a notebook or folder. Each time a student completes a skills assessment, write his score, the date, and any desired notes on his tracker.

You are hopping
with great
game-playing manners!

Language Arts Mix & Match Games • ©The Mailbox® Books • TEC61127

_____
name

I played a game today!

It was 😊 ☹ .
easy   hard

I practiced _____

_____

Language Arts Mix & Match Games • ©The Mailbox® Books • TEC61127

Look Who's Learning!

I played a game called

_____

I practiced _____

_____

Ask me about it!

Language Arts Mix & Match Games • ©The Mailbox® Books • TEC61127

Note to the teacher: Use the awards to reinforce positive behavior and communication.

Rhyming

TEC61127

Rhyming

TEC61127

Rhyming

TEC61127

Rhyming

TEC61127

Rhyming

TEC61127

Rhyming

TEC61127

Rhyming

TEC61127

Rhyming

TEC61127

Rhyming

TEC61127

Rhyming

TEC61127

Rhyming

TEC61127

Rhyming

TEC61127

Rhyming	Rhyming	Rhyming
TEC61127	TEC61127	TEC61127

Rhyming	Rhyming	Rhyming
TEC61127	TEC61127	TEC61127

Rhyming	Rhyming	Rhyming
TEC61127	TEC61127	TEC61127

Rhyming	Rhyming	Rhyming
TEC61127	TEC61127	TEC61127

Task Card

Name the rhymes.

Rhyming

TEC61127

Rhyming

TEC61127

Rhyming

TEC61127

Rhyming

TEC61127

Rhyming

TEC61127

Rhyming

TEC61127

Rhyming

TEC61127

Rhyming

TEC61127

Initial Consonants

TEC61127

Initial Consonants

TEC61127

Initial Consonants

TEC61127

Initial Consonants

TEC61127

Initial Consonants

TEC61127

Initial Consonants

TEC61127

Initial Consonants

TEC61127

Initial Consonants

TEC61127

Initial Consonants

TEC61127

Initial Consonants

TEC61127

Initial Consonants

TEC61127

Initial Consonants

TEC61127

Initial Consonants

TEC61127

Initial Consonants

TEC61127

Initial Consonants

TEC61127

Initial Consonants

TEC61127

Initial Consonants

TEC61127

Initial Consonants

TEC61127

Initial Consonants

TEC61127

Initial Consonants

TEC61127

Initial Consonants

TEC61127

Initial Consonants

TEC61127

Initial Consonants

TEC61127

Initial Consonants

TEC61127

Answer Key Card

1.	s	11.	s	21.	n
2.	f	12.	l	22.	d
3.	p	13.	t	23.	j
4.	t	14.	n	24.	h
5.	r	15.	g	25.	p
6.	w	16.	b	26.	m
7.	z	17.	d	27.	y
8.	h	18.	j	28.	w
9.	v	19.	m	29.	g
10.	b	20.	v	30.	f

Task Card

Name the beginning letter.

Initial Consonants

TEC61127

Initial Consonants

TEC61127

Initial Consonants

TEC61127

Initial Consonants

TEC61127

Initial Consonants

TEC61127

Initial Consonants

TEC61127

Initial Consonants

TEC61127

Initial Consonants

TEC61127

1. gl sl fl
2. dr tr cr
3. sk cr sp
4. st sw tw
5. sp dr sl
6. bl pl br
7. cr gr pr
8. st sw sp
9. bl pl br
10. sm sn sl
11. cl gl pl
12. cr tr dr

Initial Consonant Blends

TEC61127

Initial Consonant Blends

TEC61127

Initial Consonant Blends

TEC61127

Initial Consonant Blends

TEC61127

Initial Consonant Blends

TEC61127

Initial Consonant Blends

TEC61127

Initial Consonant Blends

TEC61127

Initial Consonant Blends

TEC61127

Initial Consonant Blends

TEC61127

Initial Consonant Blends

TEC61127

Initial Consonant Blends

TEC61127

Initial Consonant Blends

TEC61127

13 sl   sm   sn

14 fr   gr   dr

15 gl   gr   cr

16 pr   bl   br

17 sp   sc   cr

18 sp   pl   sn

19 st   tr   sm

20 cr   cl   gl

21 sw   fr   tw

22 cl   gr   cr

23 gl   gr   cl

24 sl   sp   sn

Initial Consonant Blends

TEC61127

Initial Consonant Blends

TEC61127

Initial Consonant Blends

TEC61127

Initial Consonant Blends

TEC61127

Initial Consonant Blends

TEC61127

Initial Consonant Blends

TEC61127

Initial Consonant Blends

TEC61127

Initial Consonant Blends

TEC61127

Initial Consonant Blends

TEC61127

Initial Consonant Blends

TEC61127

Initial Consonant Blends

TEC61127

Initial Consonant Blends

TEC61127

25 tr gr dr

26 pr pl br

27 pl fl fr

28 sp sl sw

29 cr gr tr

30 br pr dr

Answer Key Card

1.	fl	11.	gl	21.	sw
2.	dr	12.	tr	22.	cr
3.	sk	13.	sm	23.	gl
4.	tw	14.	fr	24.	sp
5.	sl	15.	gr	25.	dr
6.	bl	16.	br	26.	pr
7.	cr	17.	sc	27.	fl
8.	sw	18.	sp	28.	sl
9.	pl	19.	st	29.	tr
10.	sn	20.	cl	30.	br

Task Card

Name the beginning blend.

Initial Consonant Blends

TEC61127

Initial Consonant Blends

TEC61127

Initial Consonant Blends

TEC61127

Initial Consonant Blends

TEC61127

Initial Consonant Blends

TEC61127

Initial Consonant Blends

TEC61127

Initial Consonant Blends

TEC61127

Initial Consonant Blends

TEC61127

1 make	**2** that	**3** rain
4 glad	**5** back	**6** wave
7 hay	**8** cape	**9** bat
10 wax	**11** paint	**12** shade

Long *a*

TEC61127

Long *a*

TEC61127

Long *a*

TEC61127

Long *a*

TEC61127

Long *a*

TEC61127

Long *a*

TEC61127

Long *a*

TEC61127

Long *a*

TEC61127

Long *a*

TEC61127

Long *a*

TEC61127

Long *a*

TEC61127

Long *a*

TEC61127

13 past	**14** chain	**15** plane
16 tray	**17** skate	**18** rash
19 tap	**20** braid	**21** day
22 mad	**23** snack	**24** waist

Long *a*

TEC61127

Long *a*

TEC61127

Long *a*

TEC61127

Long *a*

TEC61127

Long *a*

TEC61127

Long *a*

TEC61127

Long *a*

TEC61127

Long *a*

TEC61127

Long *a*

TEC61127

Long *a*

TEC61127

Long *a*

TEC61127

Long *a*

TEC61127

25	26	27
train	fast	strait

28	29	30
has	play	frame

Answer Key Card

1.	yes	11.	yes	21.	yes
2.	no	12.	yes	22.	no
3.	yes	13.	no	23.	no
4.	no	14.	yes	24.	yes
5.	no	15.	yes	25.	yes
6.	yes	16.	yes	26.	no
7.	yes	17.	yes	27.	yes
8.	yes	18.	no	28.	no
9.	no	19.	no	29.	yes
10.	no	20.	yes	30.	yes

Task Card

Tell if the word has a long a sound as in 🍰.

Long *a*

TEC61127

Long *a*

TEC61127

Long *a*

TEC61127

Long *a*

TEC61127

Long *a*

TEC61127

Long *a*

TEC61127

Long *a*

TEC61127

Long *a*

TEC61127

Initial Consonant Digraphs

TEC61127

Initial Consonant Digraphs

TEC61127

Initial Consonant Digraphs

TEC61127

Initial Consonant Digraphs

TEC61127

Initial Consonant Digraphs

TEC61127

Initial Consonant Digraphs

TEC61127

Initial Consonant Digraphs

TEC61127

Initial Consonant Digraphs

TEC61127

Initial Consonant Digraphs

TEC61127

Initial Consonant Digraphs

TEC61127

Initial Consonant Digraphs

TEC61127

Initial Consonant Digraphs

TEC61127

Initial Consonant Digraphs

TEC61127

Initial Consonant Digraphs

TEC61127

Initial Consonant Digraphs

TEC61127

Initial Consonant Digraphs

TEC61127

Initial Consonant Digraphs

TEC61127

Initial Consonant Digraphs

TEC61127

Initial Consonant Digraphs

TEC61127

Initial Consonant Digraphs

TEC61127

Initial Consonant Digraphs

TEC61127

Initial Consonant Digraphs

TEC61127

Initial Consonant Digraphs

TEC61127

Initial Consonant Digraphs

TEC61127

Answer Key Card

1.	sh	11.	sh	21.	sh
2.	ch	12.	wh	22.	ch
3.	wh	13.	th	23.	wh
4.	th	14.	sh	24.	th
5.	sh	15.	ch	25.	th
6.	ch	16.	sh	26.	ch
7.	wh	17.	ch	27.	sh
8.	ch	18.	wh	28.	ch
9.	th	19.	wh	29.	wh
10.	th	20.	th	30.	sh

Task Card

Tell which you hear.
ch   sh
th   wh

Initial Consonant Digraphs

TEC61127

Initial Consonant Digraphs

TEC61127

Initial Consonant Digraphs

TEC61127

Initial Consonant Digraphs

TEC61127

Initial Consonant Digraphs

TEC61127

Initial Consonant Digraphs

TEC61127

Initial Consonant Digraphs

TEC61127

Initial Consonant Digraphs

TEC61127

Language Arts Mix & Match Games • ©The Mailbox® Books • TEC61127

1 ___an m z	**2** ___at w b	**3** ___ap h n
4 ___in r w	**5** ___ip l m	**6** ___ot h f
7 ___um p g	**8** ___ack v b	**9** ___ail p l
10 ___ell w r	**11** ___ine y v	**12** ___ink s h

Word Families

TEC61127

Word Families

TEC61127

Word Families

TEC61127

Word Families

TEC61127

Word Families

TEC61127

Word Families

TEC61127

Word Families

TEC61127

Word Families

TEC61127

Word Families

TEC61127

Word Families

TEC61127

Word Families

TEC61127

Word Families

TEC61127

13 ___eed	**14** ___est	**15** ___ock
v s	n d	r g
16 ___ank	**17** ___ab	**18** ___ag
b z	cr gl	bl fl
19 ___am	**20** ___ay	**21** ___op
cl br	bl pl	dr sp
22 ___ail	**23** ___ack	**24** ___unk
sw sn	tr br	pr sk

Word Families

TEC61127

Word Families

TEC61127

Word Families

TEC61127

Word Families

TEC61127

Word Families

TEC61127

Word Families

TEC61127

Word Families

TEC61127

Word Families

TEC61127

Word Families

TEC61127

Word Families

TEC61127

Word Families

TEC61127

Word Families

TEC61127

25 ___ain

ch   cl

26 ___ake

fr   sh

27 ___uck

gr   st

28 ___ing

th   sp

29 ___ill

sn   dr

30 ___ick

bl   br

Answer Key Card

1.	man	11.	vine	21.	drop
2.	bat	12.	sink	22.	snail
3.	nap	13.	seed	23.	track
4.	win	14.	nest	24.	skunk
5.	lip	15.	rock	25.	chain
6.	hot	16.	bank	26.	shake
7.	gum	17.	crab	27.	stuck
8.	back	18.	flag	28.	thing
9.	pail	19.	clam	29.	drill
10.	well	20.	play	30.	brick

Task Card

Make a word.

Word Families

TEC61127

Word Families

TEC61127

Word Families

TEC61127

Word Families

TEC61127

Word Families

TEC61127

Word Families

TEC61127

Word Families

TEC61127

Word Families

TEC61127

1
cat
bird
hat
dog

2
shirt
pants
coat
pan

3
fork
mitten
spoon
cup

4
gum
red
black
yellow

5
ball
yo-yo
fox
bike

6
farmer
flag
teacher
baker

7
tree
grass
weed
hen

8
apple
grape
book
orange

9
sock
cookie
pie
cake

10
duck
hen
rug
goose

11
morning
bugs
noon
night

12
branch
box
leaves
trunk

Vocabulary

TEC61127

Vocabulary

TEC61127

Vocabulary

TEC61127

Vocabulary

TEC61127

Vocabulary

TEC61127

Vocabulary

TEC61127

Vocabulary

TEC61127

Vocabulary

TEC61127

Vocabulary

TEC61127

Vocabulary

TEC61127

Vocabulary

TEC61127

Vocabulary

TEC61127

13
bell
plane
car
boat

14
crab
sand
shell
van

15
mom
vest
sister
uncle

16
jump
hop
red
skip

17
sled
one
seven
nine

18
pen
math
crayon
marker

19
penny
dime
cup
nickel

20
sun
rag
moon
stars

21
milk
coffee
tea
plate

22
bark
moo
hug
meow

23
raft
cat
tiger
lion

24
happy
sad
mop
mad

Vocabulary

TEC61127

Vocabulary

TEC61127

Vocabulary

TEC61127

Vocabulary

TEC61127

Vocabulary

TEC61127

Vocabulary

TEC61127

Vocabulary

TEC61127

Vocabulary

TEC61127

Vocabulary

TEC61127

Vocabulary

TEC61127

Vocabulary

TEC61127

Vocabulary

TEC61127

Language Arts Mix & Match Games • ©The Mailbox® Books • TEC61127

25 noodles pizza letter chicken

26 circle triangle square tree

27 fast hill slow quick

28 nest zipper button snap

29 hand foot bib knee

30 math reading writing wagon

Answer Key Card

1.	hat	11.	bugs	21.	plate
2.	pan	12.	box	22.	hug
3.	mitten	13.	bell	23.	raft
4.	gum	14.	van	24.	mop
5.	fox	15.	vest	25.	letter
6.	flag	16.	red	26.	tree
7.	hen	17.	sled	27.	hill
8.	book	18.	math	28.	nest
9.	sock	19.	cup	29.	bib
10.	rug	20.	rag	30.	wagon

Task Card

Tell which word does not belong.

Vocabulary

TEC61127

Vocabulary

TEC61127

Vocabulary

TEC61127

Vocabulary

TEC61127

Vocabulary

TEC61127

Vocabulary

TEC61127

Vocabulary

TEC61127

Vocabulary

TEC61127

1 stars	**2** bus	**3** car
4 twins	**5** house	**6** cherries
7 socks	**8** skates	**9** duck
10 leaf	**11** jeep	**12** hats

Plural Nouns

TEC61127

Plural Nouns

TEC61127

Plural Nouns

TEC61127

Plural Nouns

TEC61127

Plural Nouns

TEC61127

Plural Nouns

TEC61127

Plural Nouns

TEC61127

Plural Nouns

TEC61127

Plural Nouns

TEC61127

Plural Nouns

TEC61127

Plural Nouns

TEC61127

Plural Nouns

TEC61127

Language Arts Mix & Match Games • ©The Mailbox® Books • TEC61127

(13) drum	(14) fist	(15) fries
(16) ball	(17) eggs	(18) turtle
(19) boxes	(20) vest	(21) trees
(22) feet	(23) vine	(24) mice

Plural Nouns

TEC61127

Plural Nouns

TEC61127

Plural Nouns

TEC61127

Plural Nouns

TEC61127

Plural Nouns

TEC61127

Plural Nouns

TEC61127

Plural Nouns

TEC61127

Plural Nouns

TEC61127

Plural Nouns

TEC61127

Plural Nouns

TEC61127

Plural Nouns

TEC61127

Plural Nouns

TEC61127

25 dice	26 bag	27 teeth
28 children	29 farm	30 dress

Answer Key Card

1.	yes	11.	no	21.	yes
2.	no	12.	yes	22.	yes
3.	no	13.	no	23.	no
4.	yes	14.	no	24.	yes
5.	no	15.	yes	25.	yes
6.	yes	16.	no	26.	no
7.	yes	17.	yes	27.	yes
8.	yes	18.	no	28.	yes
9.	no	19.	yes	29.	no
10.	no	20.	no	30.	no

Task Card

Tell if the word means more than one.

Plural Nouns

TEC61127

Plural Nouns

TEC61127

Plural Nouns

TEC61127

Plural Nouns

TEC61127

Plural Nouns

TEC61127

Plural Nouns

TEC61127

Plural Nouns

TEC61127

Plural Nouns

TEC61127

Language Arts Mix & Match Games • ©The Mailbox® Books • TEC61127

Antonyms

TEC61127

Antonyms

TEC61127

Antonyms

TEC61127

Antonyms

TEC61127

Antonyms

TEC61127

Antonyms

TEC61127

Antonyms

TEC61127

Antonyms

TEC61127

Antonyms

TEC61127

Antonyms

TEC61127

Antonyms

TEC61127

Antonyms

TEC61127

13 in out

14 on off

15 smile yell

16 tree nap

17 dry wet

18 hard soft

19 open closed

20 rip pull

21 fast slow

22 brush curl

23 prince king

24 hot cold

Antonyms

TEC61127

Antonyms

TEC61127

Antonyms

TEC61127

Antonyms

TEC61127

Antonyms

TEC61127

Antonyms

TEC61127

Antonyms

TEC61127

Antonyms

TEC61127

Antonyms

TEC61127

Antonyms

TEC61127

Antonyms

TEC61127

Antonyms

TEC61127

25	26	27
short tall	night day	east hit

28	29	30
big little	sick nurse	over under

Answer Key Card

1.	yes	11.	yes	21.	yes
2.	no	12.	no	22.	no
3.	yes	13.	yes	23.	no
4.	no	14.	yes	24.	yes
5.	yes	15.	no	25.	yes
6.	no	16.	no	26.	yes
7.	yes	17.	yes	27.	no
8.	yes	18.	yes	28.	yes
9.	yes	19.	yes	29.	no
10.	no	20.	no	30.	yes

Task Card

Tell if the words are opposites.

Antonyms

TEC61127

Antonyms

TEC61127

Antonyms

TEC61127

Antonyms

TEC61127

Antonyms

TEC61127

Antonyms

TEC61127

Antonyms

TEC61127

Antonyms

TEC61127

Game Markers

Cut out the game markers. Fold the cutouts along the thin lines, keeping the artwork to the outside. Store each set of game markers with the corresponding gameboard.

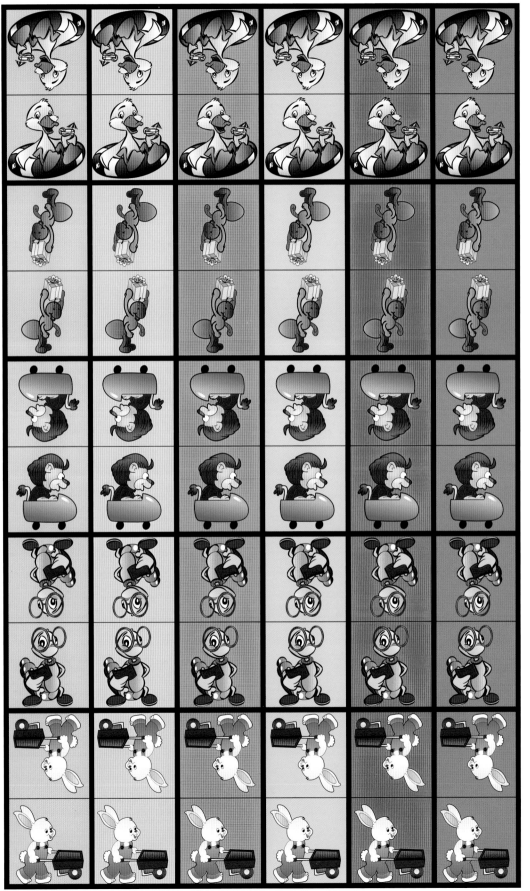

Use with "Relaxing Ride."

Use with "Party Time!"

Use with "Loop-the-Loop."

Use with "Book Buddies."

Use with "Happy Hopper."

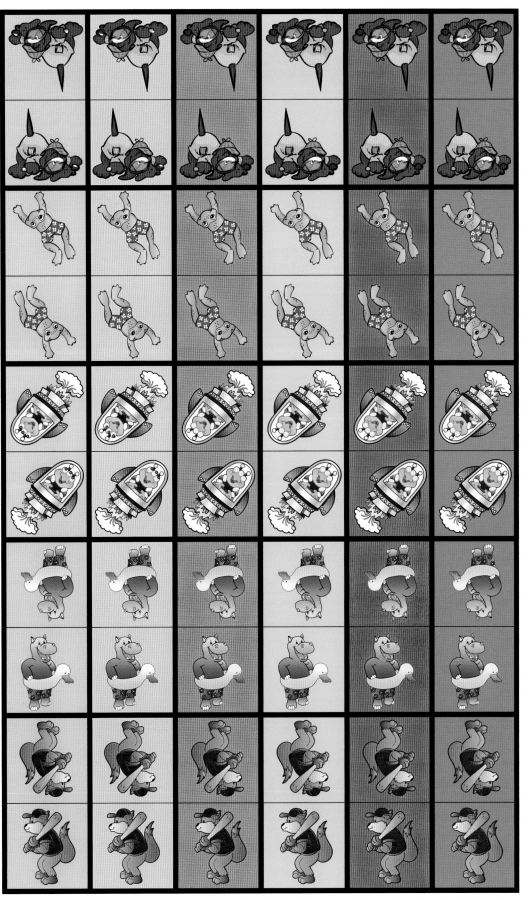

Use with
"Super Sleuth."

Use with
"Leaping on
Lily Pads."

Use with
"To the Moon!"

Use with
"Going for a
Swim."

Use with
"Play Ball!"

TEC61127   TEC61127   TEC61127   TEC61127   TEC61127   TEC61127

TEC61127   TEC61127   TEC61127   TEC61127   TEC61127   TEC61127

TEC61127   TEC61127   TEC61127   TEC61127   TEC61127   TEC61127

TEC61127   TEC61127   TEC61127   TEC61127   TEC61127   TEC61127

TEC61127   TEC61127   TEC61127   TEC61127   TEC61127   TEC61127

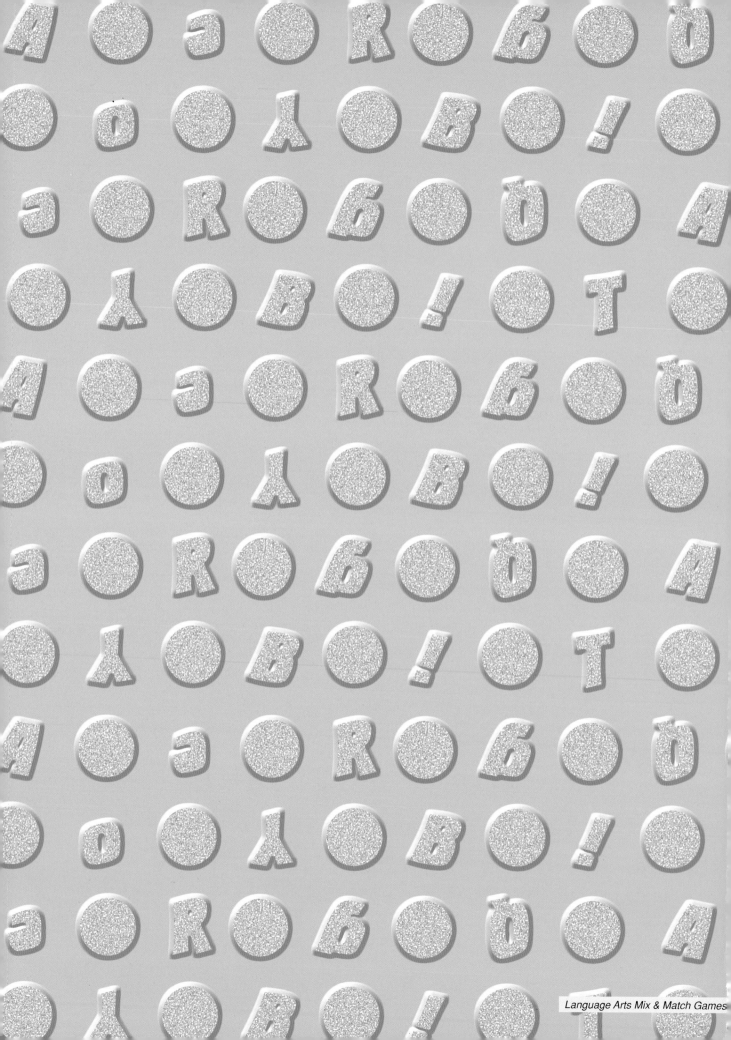

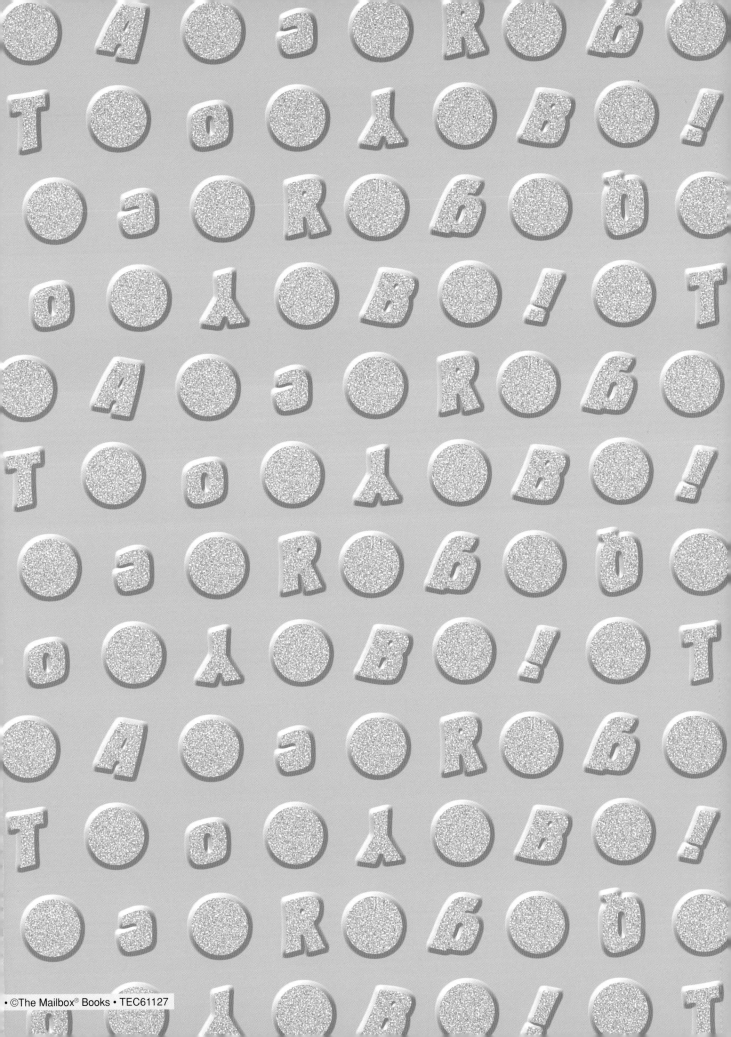

Party Time!

START

Slide on a
vine.
Move ahead
one space.

Hide fro...
an ante...

Miss
one
turn.

Directions fo...

1. Put the task card...
2. Stack the game ...
3. Put your markers...
4. In turn, draw a ga...
   answer.
5. If your answer is...
   and move.
6. The first player to...

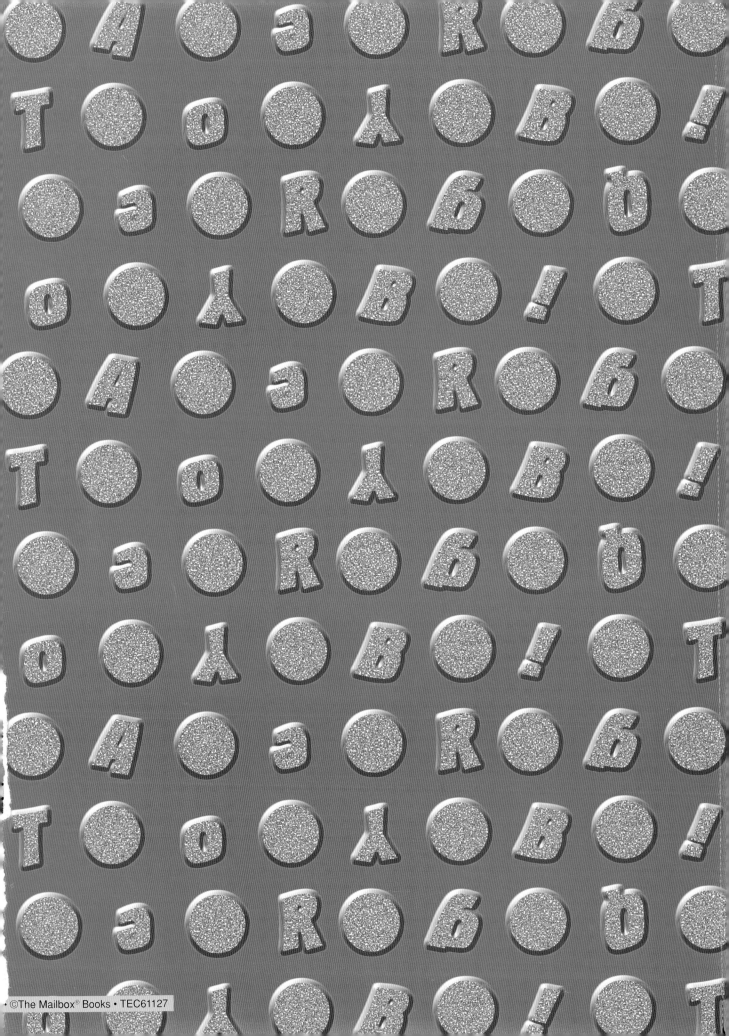

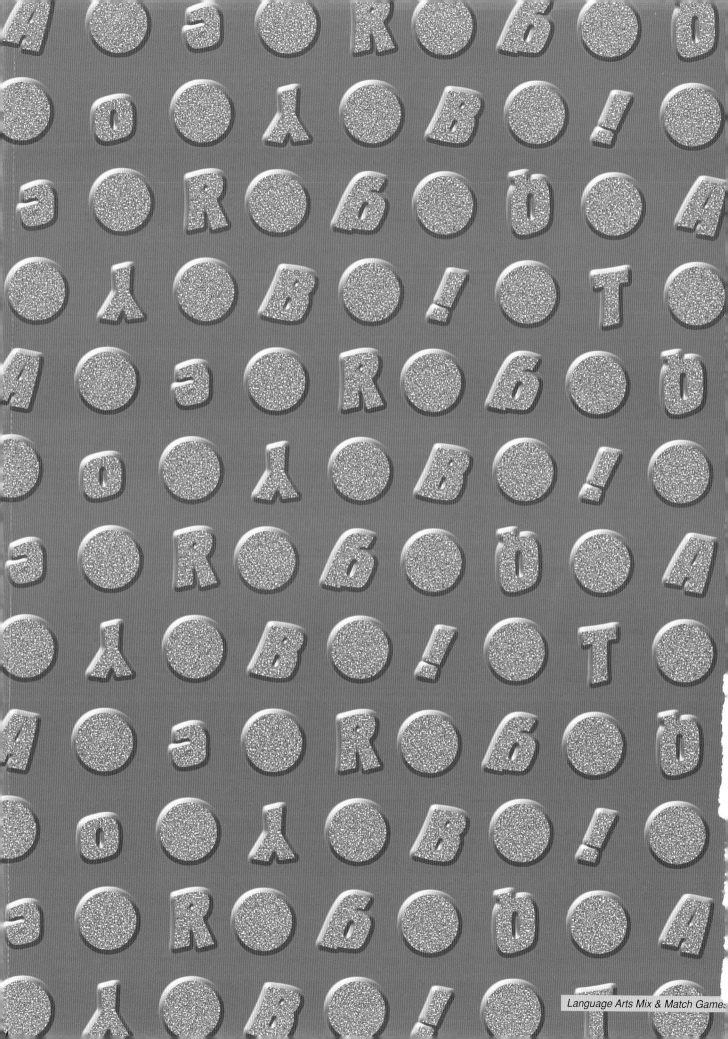

Buddies

Put task card here.

...or two players:

... the gameboard.

...ds facedown.

... START.

...e card and give your

...rrect, roll the die

...ach FINISH wins.

FINISH

Drop your card.

Library Card

Move back one space.

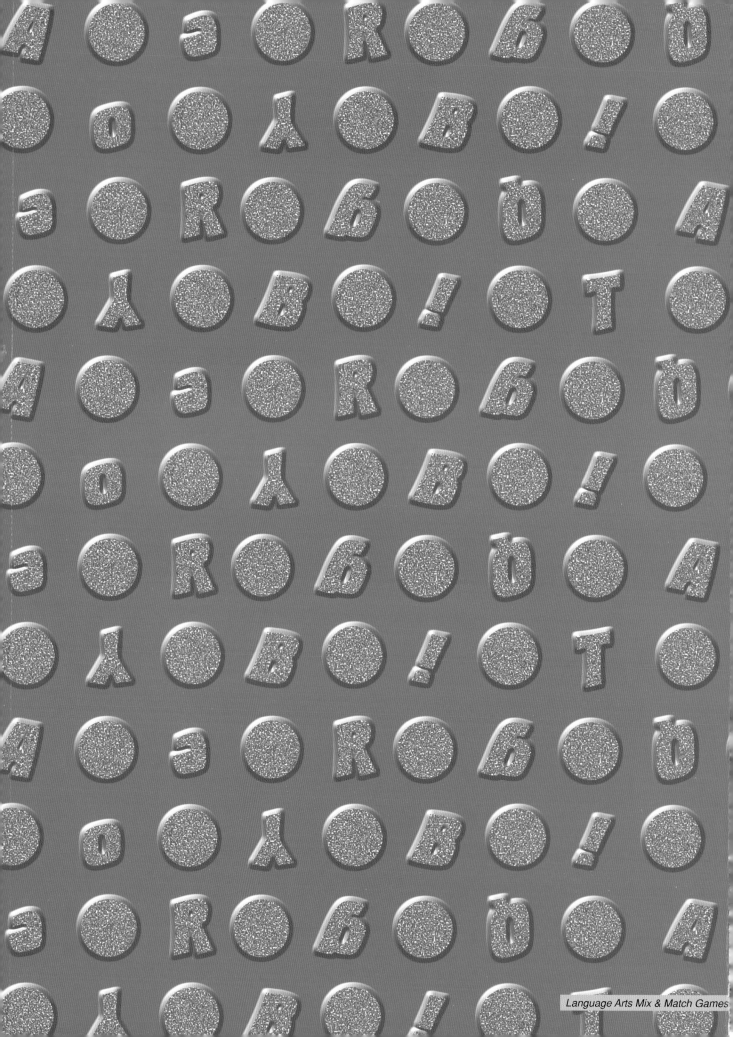

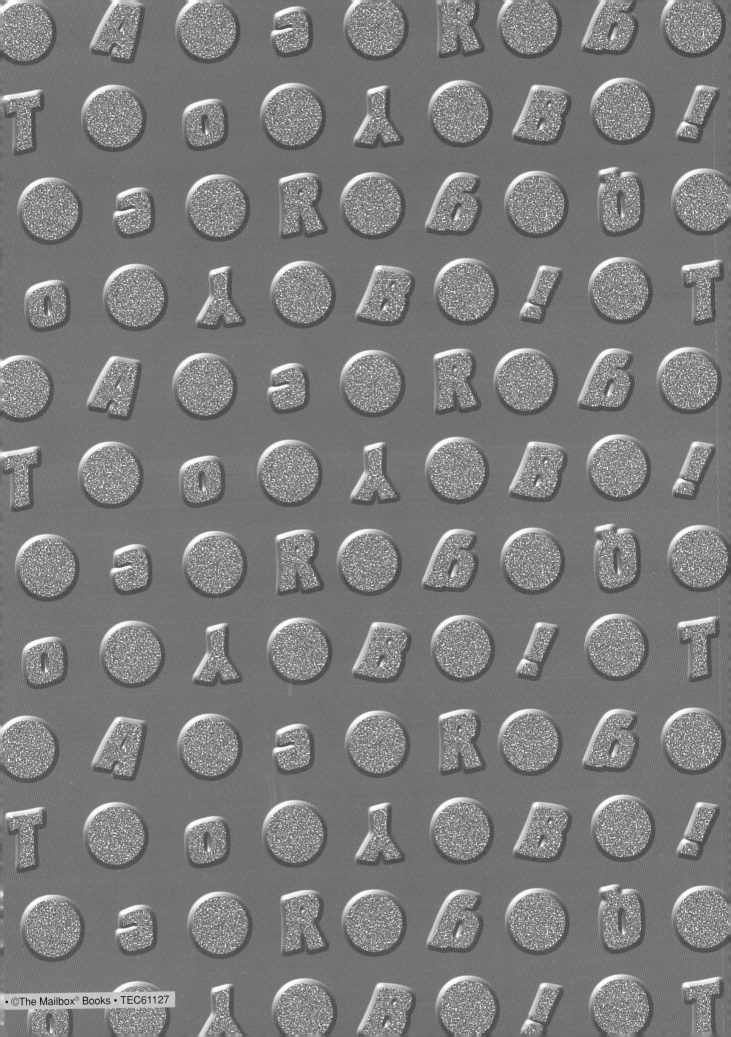

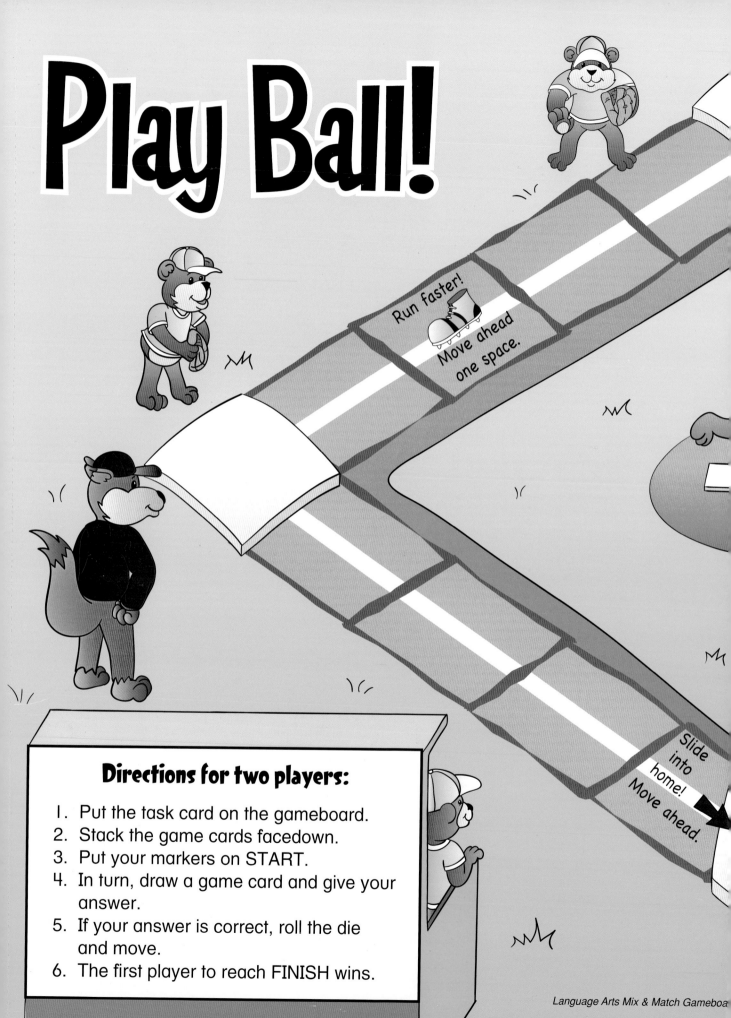

Play Ball!

Run faster!
Move ahead one space.

Slide into home!
Move ahead.

Directions for two players:

1. Put the task card on the gameboard.
2. Stack the game cards facedown.
3. Put your markers on START.
4. In turn, draw a game card and give your answer.
5. If your answer is correct, roll the die and move.
6. The first player to reach FINISH wins.

Language Arts Mix & Match Gameboa

pper

Put task card here.

You see a carrot.

Move ahead one space.

FINISH

Directions for two players:

1. Put the task card on the gameboard.
2. Stack the game cards facedown.
3. Put your markers on START.
4. In turn, draw a game card and give your answer.
5. If your answer is correct, roll the die and move.
6. The first player to reach FINISH wins.

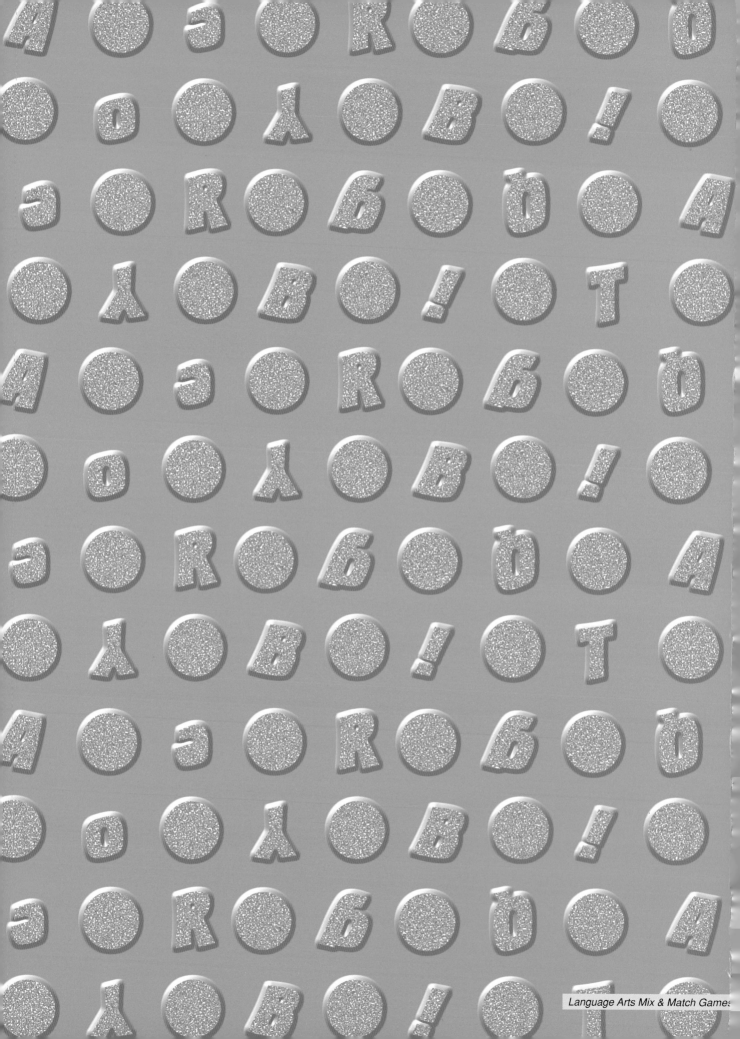

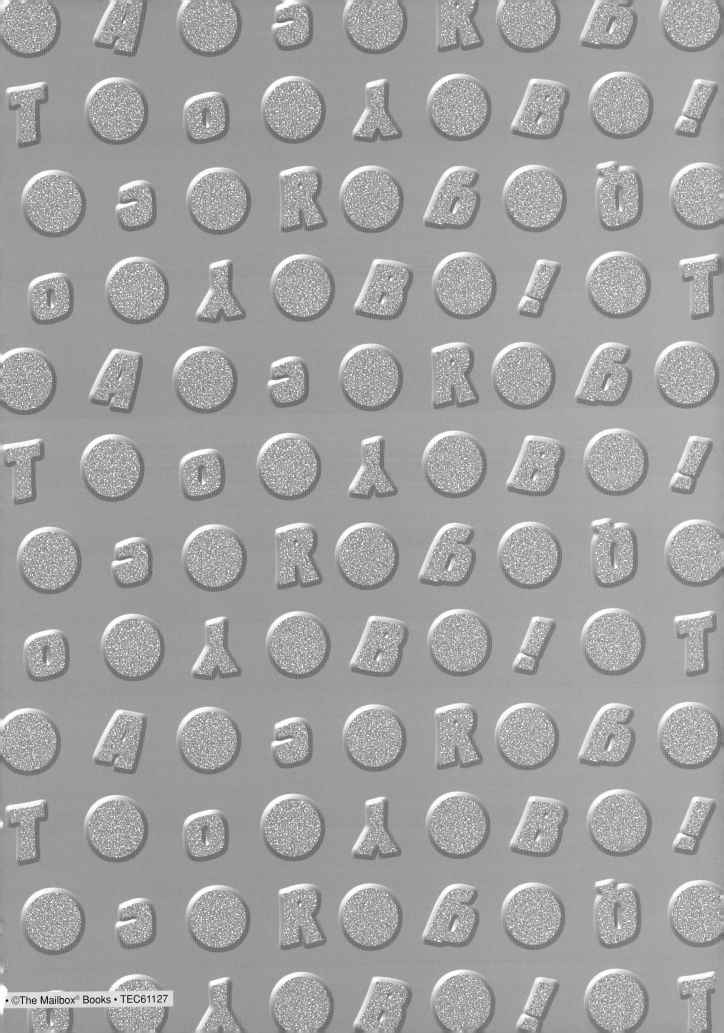

HaPPy Ho...

Stop to n...

Miss one...

Great hopping!

Move ahead one
space.

START